D1639635
PARADE OF FLOATS
BARGAINS
FLOWER ARRANGING
THIS WAY
LADIES CIRCLE
£5.99

DENNIS the MENACE
THIS CROOK BELONGS TO DAD

Printed and Published by D. C. THOMSON & CO., LTD., 185 Fleet Street, London EC4A 2HS.

ISBN 0 85116 743 8

THE MENACE MINDER!

JUST A SECOND, WALTER!
SKIP

D-DON'T M-MENACE ME, P-PLEASE!
I'M NOT GOING TO MENACE YOU...

... I'M GOING TO STOP YOU CATCHING COLD! I'M PROTECTING YOU!

B-BUT IT'S THE MIDDLE OF SUMMER!
CAN'T TAKE CHANCES— YOU KNOW WHAT SUMMER'S LIKE!

NOW I'M GOING TO ESCORT YOU TO SCHOOL!

I CAN'T SEE BECAUSE OF THIS PESKY BALACLAVA!
OOPS! GOT TO HURRY!

STOMP
H-HE'S MADE IT!

SLIDE
BUT I HAVEN'T!

SPLUTCH!

BUT IT'LL BE WORTH IT!

ZOOM
H-HE'S GOING TO HIT WALTER!

B-BUT NOT IF I CAN HELP IT!
ZOOM

SQUASHED
YAHOO!
ST-STILL, IT'LL B-BE WORTH IT!

IN CLASS—
BECAUSE I'M SITTING RIGHT BEHIND WALTER! JUST RIGHT FOR COPYING!
HERE ARE YOUR TEST PAPERS...
... ALL EXCEPT WALTER— HE'S TOO CLEVER FOR THIS TEST!
ALL MY HARD WORK FOR NOTHING!
SLAP SLAP
TESTING! TESTING! ~ OVER THE PAGE!

TESTING! TESTING!
TEST DRIVE
ARMY
ARMY
HA-HA! THE COLONEL'S JEEP HANDLES WELL!
EEKUMS! OUR TEDDY BEAR'S PICNIC — RUINED!
SPLART!
WHEEE
ACE FLYING, HUH?
SPLUTCH!
BYOING!
BONG!
VAROOOOM!
YAARG
GLU
COMPOST HEAP
TEST PILOT

TEST MATCH
SWISH!
HOWZAT?
THWACK!
BOOT
STINK BOMB
PONG
NASTY NIFF
STINK
SHRIEK!
WAAH!
CRICKET PAVILION
EST TUBE
BATS' NOSTRILS AND LIQUID WOTSIT!
POUR
GNEE-HEE! REALLY KETCHUP AND JELLY!
POUR
GLUG! GLUB!
TEST CARD
DAD SAID WE'D TESTED HIS PATIENCE TOO FAR! WE'RE GROUNDED! BAH!
TEST CARD
GNUH! GNOTHING ON TELLY!

SERVES HIM RIGHT!

YOU CAN'T PLAY BECAUSE YOU DON'T HAVE A TENNIS RACKET—SO THERE!
TAP
TAP
SOON GET ONE! FETCH, GNASHER!
ZOOM

TEA
CRACK
I'M SURE THERE WAS A PAN THERE!
SNATCH
SIZZLE

YOU STILL CAN'T PLAY—THAT'S A FRYING PAN—OUCH!
CRUNCH
WAP
IT'S A MENACE RACKET—GET OVER THERE AND I'LL PLAY YOU BOTH!

MY SERVICE! IT'LL BE A FAST ONE!
TOSS

B-BE G-GENTLE W-WITH US, P-PLEASE!

TOPPLE
WHAP

HMMM! SOME FAST FIRST-AID SERVICE NEEDED HERE!

STOP COMPLAINING—I'M TRYING TO HELP! SNIGGER!
EEK!
BAH, DOSE!
TUG
TUG

GRUNT! IT'S A STUBBORN LITTLE DEVIL—HAVE TO TRY SOMETHING ELSE!
...NNNNG!
HEAVE

THIS SNEEZING POWDER SHOULD DO THE TRICK!
SHAKE
D-DONE IT!
PYOINNG
AAA...

BAH! I'M STUCK AGAIN!
CHOOOO
WHAP

WAIT A MINUTE—WHAT'S THAT?
DENNIS! DENNIS!
IT'S A DENNIS RACKET!

I NEED A REALLY FAST SERVICE NOW...

... A FAST BUS SERVICE TO GET ME AWAY FROM MUM!
BUS STOP
HEH! HEH!
TREMBLE
HOI! YOU PINCHED MY FRYING PAN!

MORE SPORTING LAUGHS NOW WITH...
...ANYONE FOR DENNIS?
LINE JUDGE
OUT! AND I SENTENCE YOU TO TWENTY YEARS HOMEWORK!
GNEE-HEE!
JUICE
JUICE
PLOP!
THE FIRST SET
OLIVE'S BLACMANGE
YUP! IT'S ALMOST SET!
WAH!
SLOP
TUG!
15-LOVE
BOKE!

BOOM -DA- BOOM
WHAP
OO! MY POOR EARS! WHAT A RACKET!
TENNIS RACKET
EUCE
ICE, ACTUALLY! HAH-HAH!
EEK!
SPRAY!
UMPIRE'S CHAIR
VERY COMFY! DON'T YOU AGREE, WALTER?
JUICE
NNNGH! NNNGH!
STUCK FAST!
O! I LOVE LL FIFTEEN OF YOU!

PLANELY A PEST!

PYOING!
I MAY NOT HAVE MANY HAIRS LEFT ON TOP, BUT I'M VERY PROUD OF THEM!

WAH! MY LITTLE BEAUTIES—GONE!
ZOOM!
Z-I-P!

STICK DOWN
I'M HAVING GREAT FUN WITH THIS RADIO-CONTROLLED PLANE!
ZOOM!
ZOOM!
PRANG!

ZOOM!
DROOP
SKIP
SPLUTCH!
WAH!
HAR-HAR!
GNASHEE!

OO! HOW PRETTY!

ZOOM!
WOW! THAT'S NO BUTTERFLY!

ZOOM!

SQUEAL! PUT ME DOWN! PUT ME DOWN!
LIFT

YOU HORRID ROTTER! I'LL CATCH A COLDIE-WOLDIE!
HAR-HAR!

AAAA—
HAR! HAR!

CHOO!
PRANG!
BLAST

YEOWK!
TOSS

CATCH
WICKED TEE-HEE!

NO! NO! ANYTHING BUT THIS!
EAU DE COLOGNE
LOVELY AROMAS
SWEET SMELLS
PERFUME FACTORY
WAY IN
PRESS
ZOOM!
CAN'T WATCH
WONDERFUL MODEL THIS! TEE-HEE!

THUMPING THILLY!

THUMP!
THUMP!

WHAT ARE YOU UP TO?
OOPS! THOUGHT I WAS STANDING ON A HILL.

THIS IS THE WAY WE RABBITS TALK TO EACH OTHER.
OINKEH?
THUMP!
THUMP!

HERE'S YOUR ORDER FROM THE RABBIT CARRY OUT.
OIKWOW!

MUST TRY SOME RABBIT TALK.
THUMP!
THUMP!

BUNNYOOH!
THUMP!
SHAKE

WHAT DID THAT MEAN?
GASP! IT MEANT "EARTHQUAKE!"
DAZED

I'LL TRY SHOUTING.

GIGANTIC WHUMP!

WHAT DID THAT MEAN?
IT MEANT . . .

. . . BEWARE OF FALLING CHIMNEY POTS.
ERK!
CRASH!

I THINK THAT THUMPING MEANS DAD'S ANGRY.
ZOOM!
THUMP!

DENNIS and GNASHER are—
OUT OF THEIR TREE!
Dennis's Treehouse
WAHEY! HIYA, READERS.
GNOO-HOO!

OUR TREE HOUSE IS BRILLIANT — BUT IT NEEDS A FEW RUNNING REPAIRS.
Dennis's Treehouse
GNYEAH!
SNAP!
SNAP!

So —
HEE-HEE!
SPIN — SPIN
VERY GOOD, WALTER!
SPIFFING SPINS!
EEKUMS!
WHEEE
GNASH!
CHOMP!
WHEE
ERK!
DOOFYAH!
GNEE-HEE!
WHEE
SLAM!
BEANO CASTL
BOUNCE
PLONK
YOU SEE, WE NEED ALL THAT WOOD FOR OUR RUNNING REPAIRS!
OO-ER! KNOW WHY THEY'RE CALLED RUNNING REPAIRS?
GNOT A CLUE!

TA FOR THE FLOORBOARDS!
And —
ZOOM
THUD! THUD!
BEANOTOWN CASTLE
ONE DOES ENJOY RE-ENACTING THE 12TH CENTURY SIEGE OF BEANOTOWN CASTLE!
Then —
TIME FOR A NAP, METHINKS.
YEOW!
GOT THEM! AND GOT HIM!
TUG!
TUG!
MENACES!
RUN! OR WE'LL NEED REPAIRED!
BOUNDERS!
GNULP!
ZOOM

UP YOUR JUMPER!

MY JERSEY'S MADE OF SPECIALLY TOUGH MATERIAL!
BARBED-WIRE HANGER

I'VE HIRED THIS SPECIALLY TRAINED GUARD DOG TO SORT OUT HORRID DENNIS!
RUFF! RUFF!

SEEK, RIPPER!
RUFF! RUFF!
ZOOM!

CHOMP!

HAW-HAW! SAVED BY MY TOUGH JERSEY!
OOOO! MY DOG!
GNASH! GNASH!
SHLURP!

HANDS UP!
PROD

THIS IS THE ONLY WAY I CAN GET THIS JERSEY OFF HIM TO BE WASHED!
SNATCH

B-BUT, MUM...

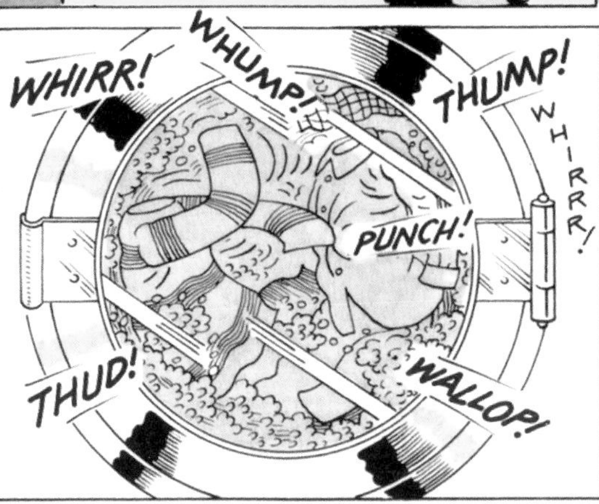
WHIRR!
WHUMP!
THUMP!
WHIRRR!
PUNCH!
THUD!
WALLOP!

THEN–
WAH!
YOU SHOULDN'T HAVE PUT MY JERSEY IN WITH THAT SOFT STUFF, MUM!

SHORTLY–
MY JERSEY AND I ARE PLAYING FOOTBALL!

OH, NO! BALL BOY'S SURE TO SCORE, UNLESS....

PHEEP!
EH?
PUSH

EH?
GOAL!
THUD!
ERK!
READER'S VOICE
GASP! THAT'S SOME JERSEY, DENNIS!
IT SURE IS, READER....

....BUT GNASHER'S ALSO SOME DOG!
HEH-HEH! I WAS HAVING A GNAP UNDER THAT WARM JERSEY!
BAH!
HEH! HEH!
ZOOM!

SCHOOL'S OUT FOR TROUBLE!

WHAT A BUNCH OF WIMPS!
SNIFF! IGNORE THOSE RUFFIANS! WE'LL BE LATE FOR OUR CHARM SCHOOL FOR YOUNG GENTLEMEN!

SCHOOL FOR YOUNG GENTLEMEN
FEES £5 PER LESSON
THERE'S MONEY TO BE MADE IN THIS TEACHING LARK!
SO-
SCHOOL FOR YOUNG MENACES
FEES 10p PER LESSON
BANG!
BANG!
CLICK!

SCHOOL FOR YOUNG MENACES
FEES 10p PER LESSON
FLIP
CHINK

TSK! YOU'RE TOO NEAT TO BE MENACES!

...SO WE'LL UNTIDY YOU A BIT - THIS IS A GOOD MENACING TRICK TOO...
WAH!
EEK!
SPLASH
SPLODGE
MUDDY POOLS →

EEK!
...AND THIS WILL FINISH THE JOB!
BIN
GNASHEE!

MUCH BETTER! NOW LET'S SEE HOW YOU WALK! QUICK-SLOUCH!

HOPELESS! TOO NEAT! CURLY, COLLECT THEIR SHOE LACES AND BELTS!

SLOUCH
STOOP
SHUFFLE
SHUFFLE
SHUFFLE
THAT'S THE WAY A MENACE WALKS!

YOUR LAST LESSON IS HOW TO EAT LIKE A MENACE - OBSERVE!
SNIFF SNIFF

HEH-HEH! HERE ENDETH THE LESSON!
CHOMP!
PUSH
TOPPLE

LATER-

A GOOD DAY'S WORK! LOTS OF NEW MENACES AND WHAT ARE WE GOING TO DO WITH ALL THIS CASH?

THEN-
TURN OUR KIDDIES INTO MENACES, WOULD YOU?
ZOOM
ULP! NOW I KNOW WHAT TO DO WITH THE CASH...

SCHOOL FOR YOUNG GENTLEMEN
...FEES FOR HERE! IT'S THE LAST PLACE THOSE PARENTS WOULD LOOK FOR US!

GNASHER'S BIG CAT SAFARI

1 THE LEOPARD

GNEE HEE-HEE!

GET OFF MY BACK, MAN!

RIDE 'EM, DOGGY!

COINS IN HERE
I WANT A GO ON THAT, DAD.

I'VE NO COINS, GNIPPER.
DIZZY
COINS IN HERE
SEARCH!

I KNOW HOW TO GET SOME.
TUG
COINS IN HERE

COINS IN HERE

WOW! I'VE NEVER RIDDEN A DOG BEFORE.
COINS IN HERE

SHOVE
COINS IN HERE
GNI'VE GOT A COIN NOW.

WAHEY! THIS IS FUN.
BACK!
COINS IN HERE

But —
FLATTEN

HMPH! CHEAP MUCK — NOT BUILT TO LAST!
ANGRY→
DAZED!

OOYAH!
NO-ONE CALLS MY DAD CHEAP MUCK AND GETS AWAY WITH IT.
BITE

I'LL NEED THIS NOW.
REMOVE

DON'T WORRY, DAD — SOON HAVE YOU IN HOSPITAL.
EEAWWEEAW
AMBULANCE
BRRM
COIN IN HERE
VROOM

HISTORY
MYSTERY!

HISTORY NEXT...
OH, BOY!
DENNIS INTERESTED IN HISTORY? I DON'T BELIEVE IT!
READER'S VOICE

... STARTING WITH CAPTAIN TEACH, ALIAS "BLACKBEARD"!
BLACKBEARD
THIS HISTORY'S ALL ABOUT PIRATES SWASHING THEIR BUCKLES AND THINGS—SO ZIP YOUR LIP, READER!
SNIFF! VERY SORRY, I'M SURE!
READER'S VOICE

BACK HOME—
SHE'S ALMOST READY TO LAUNCH, GNASHER! YO-HO-HO AND A BOTTLE OF RASPBERRY FIZZY POP!
HAMMER!
SAW!
BANG!
THUD!
Dennis's shed

CAPTAIN BLACKHAIR, THE SCOURGE OF THE SEVEN STREETS, SETS SAIL! STEADY AS SHE GOES, FIRST MATE GNASHER!
ZOOM!

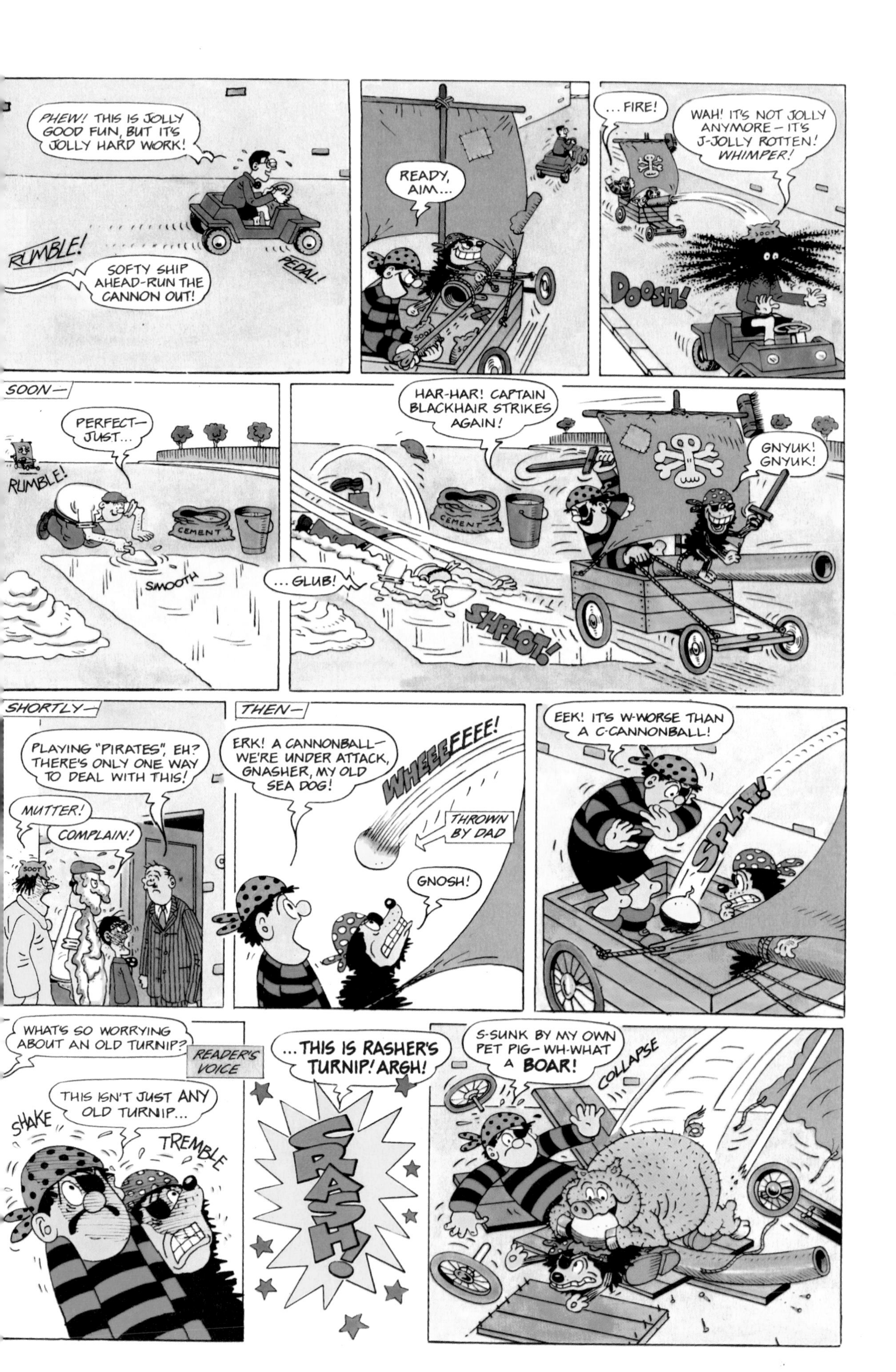
PHEW! THIS IS JOLLY GOOD FUN, BUT IT'S JOLLY HARD WORK!
RUMBLE!
PEDAL!
SOFTY SHIP AHEAD-RUN THE CANNON OUT!
READY, AIM...
SOOT
...FIRE!
WAH! IT'S NOT JOLLY ANYMORE – IT'S J-JOLLY ROTTEN! WHIMPER!
DOOSH!
SOOT
SOON—
PERFECT— JUST...
RUMBLE!
CEMENT
SMOOTH
HAR-HAR! CAPTAIN BLACKHAIR STRIKES AGAIN!
GNYUK! GNYUK!
CEMENT
...GLUB!
SHPLOT!
SHORTLY—
PLAYING "PIRATES", EH? THERE'S ONLY ONE WAY TO DEAL WITH THIS!
MUTTER!
COMPLAIN!
SOOT
THEN—
ERK! A CANNONBALL— WE'RE UNDER ATTACK, GNASHER, MY OLD SEA DOG!
WHEEEFFEEE!
THROWN BY DAD
GNOSH!
EEK! IT'S W-WORSE THAN A C-CANNONBALL!
SPLAT!
WHAT'S SO WORRYING ABOUT AN OLD TURNIP?
READER'S VOICE
THIS ISN'T JUST ANY OLD TURNIP...
SHAKE
TREMBLE
...THIS IS RASHER'S TURNIP! ARGH!
CRASH!
S-SUNK BY MY OWN PET PIG– WH-WHAT A BOAR!
COLLAPSE

THE MENACE'S APPRENTICE
I WANT YOU TO KEEP YOUR YOUNG COUSIN HAPPY FOR A WHILE, DENNIS.
SIGH! OK, DAD!
MY HERO!

I'M GOING TO SCARE PEOPLE WITH MY MASK!
GREAT! AN APPRENTICE MENACE!
SO—
BOO!
GIGGLE!
WHAT A SHAME! EVEN THE PRINCE OF SOFTIES IS LAUGHING AT MY COUSIN!
RECKON I'LL JUST HAVE TO GIVE MY KID COUSIN A HELPING HAND!
Dennis's shed
PEAS
WATER

SOON—
BOO!
DON'T MAKE ME...

... F-FAINT!
I DID IT! I SCARED HIM!

JUST DO MY GOOD DEED AND WAKEN BERTIE UP.
SQUIRT!

HERE COMES SOFTY WALTER, BUT IF I SCARE HIM, HE'LL JUST LAUGH AT ME AGAIN.
NO, HE WON'T...

... NOT WITH THIS WORM DOWN HIS NECK!
BOO!
HA-HA...

...ARGH!
PLOP!

HE'S SCARED TOO — I'M A REAL MENACE NOW!
WAH!

LATER—
I'VE HAD NOTHING BUT COMPLAINTS ABOUT YOU! YOU'RE GOING TO BE...
ERK!
WAIT!
READER'S VOICE—

DENNIS WAS ONLY KEEPING HIS YOUNG COUSIN HAPPY— HONESTLY!
READER'S VOICE
HE WAS?

SO—
GROAN! I'M BEING SENT EARLY TO BED...

... WITH MY SUPPER! YIPPEEYAHOO!
WELL, I DIDN'T KNOW WHETHER TO PUNISH HIM OR REWARD HIM, READERS!
BEANO

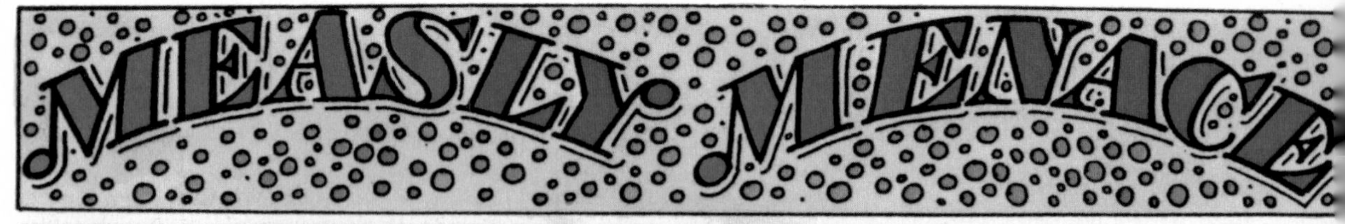
MEASLY MENACE

JUST OFF TO MENACE-
ER-I MEAN PLAY, MUM.

HOLD IT-WHAT ARE THESE SPOTS?
EH?

ENTER THE DOCTOR-
OUTER MONGOLIAN MEASLES-
BED, YOUNG MAN!
AW!

THE NEWS SPREADS-
YAHOO! WE'RE SAFE FROM THE MENACE FOR A WHILE!
THE MENACE CAN'T MENACE!
TA-RA!
HMPH!
GNMPH!

CRUMBS! I'M BORED — I'LL HAVE TO LIVEN THINGS UP! DAD, I WANT TO SEE YOU!

YES? WHAT IS IT?
MY HOT WATER BOTTLE ISN'T! IT'S ICY COLD...

...FEEL!
GLUB!
SCOOSH!

I WAS RIGHT-COLD, ISN'T IT?
SO IT SHOULD BE-I PUT IT ON THE WINDOW LEDGE!
BRRRGRRR!

LATER-
HERE'S YOUR DINNER, DENNIS!
HUH! I'M BORED-NOT HUNGRY!

THINK I'LL GO FOR THE WORLD RECORD FOR...

...HIGHEST SAUSAGE AND MASH! AW, IT'S STUCK! SNIGGER!
SPLAT!
THUMP!

WHAT'S ALL THIS THUMPING? WHAT'S GOING ON?
THAT SHOULD BE...

...WHAT'S COMING DOWN!
SPLOTCH!
HOWL!

MUCH LATER-
YOU'RE COMPLETELY CURED, YOUNG MAN.
H-HE IS!
GREAT!

WHOOPEE! HE'LL BE OUT OF THE HOUSE! NO MORE MENACING FOR A WHILE!
CLANG!
WAVE
EVER GET THE FEELING THAT NOBODY LOVES YOU, READERS?

THERE'S A
FIRST TIME FOR
EVERYTHING
COCK-A-DOODLE
DOO
FIRST LIGHT
QUILTED COSY HOTTY FOR A CISSY BOYS' BOTTY
FIRST FOOT
HAPPY NEW YEAR!
STOMP!
FIRST CLASS POST
'AT A FIRST CLASS GOAL POST!

FIRST FLOOR
SNAP!
SNAP!
DOWN ESCALATOR
'EE-'EE! WALTER WANNA GET ON FIRST FLOOR!
FIRST AID
SPIN
'OO NEEDS A SPINNING TOP?
BEA! DID YOU DO NAUGHTY THINGS TO WALTER?
ANOTHER MINER'S WORLD GIFT
60 WATT BULB
THE THIRD DEGREE
LIKKLE ME??? ME DON'T KNOW THE FIRST FING ABOUT IT!
N.P.

THE NORMAN CONQUEST PART 1

At home
Tum-tee . . .
EEK! I'm sure there was a clothes rope there this morning!
Chuckle! You can't soak me because there's no puddle! I'm not daft! Heh-heh-heh!
BUS STOP
Hey!
Want to bet?
BUS STOP
Wah!
Just make sure it's nice and tight so you can't escape.
C — compost? Y — you wouldn't d — dare!
PONG!
You think not?
Ooo!
Well, think again!
Anyway, I won't get splashed — that bus will slow down for the bus stop!
BUS STOP
It would . . .
. . . if there was a bus stop here!
BUS STOP
Ulp!
So —
Snigger!
SPLATTER!
BUS STOP
The only thing really nasty about you now, Norman, is your SMELL!
Sob!
Gnot gnice!

'WEIGHT' TO GO!
GROAN! I'D EVEN PAY TO LOSE WEIGHT!
HMM! GIVES ME AN IDEA.
LATER—
I KNOW I SHOULDN'T, BUT WILL I, OR WON'T I?
DROOL
YOU WON'T!
EEK!
SPLUDGE!
OINKSLURP!
GNIPULP!
GNULP!

THAT NIGHT—
GIBBER!
FRUIT

I C-CAN'T STAND IT— I'VE GOT TO HAVE FOOD!
KITCHE
RUMBLE!

BUT—
HOWL!
PLOP!
SOOT BOMB
SWOOSH!
FRIDGE
PING! PING!

WAH!
HEH! I KNEW SHE'D TRY SOMETHING LIKE THAT!
ZOOM!

LATER—
TUM-TEE-TUM!
COOKING SMELL
SIZZLE!
OVEN CHIPS

KITCHEN
COOKING SMELLS
MORE COOKING SMELLS

... HOW SWEET— YOU'VE COOKED A BIG BREAKFAST, DENNIS!
ALL THE FOOD IN THE HOUSE AND IT'S ALL FOR...
SLURP!

... RASHER!
NO!
OPEN
STAMP

THAT DOES IT— NO POCKET-MONEY THIS WEEK!
BEFORE YOU SAY THAT...

... WHY NOT CHECK YOUR WEIGHT?
WHY, I'VE LOST LOTS— DOUBLE POCKET-MONEY THIS WEEK!
BOYLP!
LEAP
PUSH

IT STILL WASN'T A GOOD IDEA— MUM LOST SO MUCH WEIGHT...

GNASH! PUFF! CAN'T KEEP UP!
... SHE'S FIT ENOUGH TO CATCH ME WHEN I DO SOMETHING BAD!
LEAP
LEAP

RASHER PIGS OUT!

CAFE
OPEN
HUMANS ARE DISGUSTING EATERS.

Look—
CHOMP!
SQUIRT!
SPLAT!

CAFE
OPEN
I'LL SHOW THEM THE CORRECT WAY TO EAT A JAM DOUGHNUT.

FIRST GET INTO POSITION . . .
SNIFF!
SNIFF!

. . . AND SUCK IT ON TO YOUR SNOUT.
SUCK!

THEN PUNCTURE WITH A TUSK.
PRANG

AND SUCK THE JAM OUT.
SUCK!

REMOVE THE SUGAR FROM THE OUTSIDE . . .

. . . THEN EAT. CHOMP.
CHOMP!

MUST TRY THIS! TWO MORE JAM DOUGHNUTS, WAITER.

BEFORE TRYING THIS, READERS, DO ONE IMPORTANT THING . . .
SHAKE!

MUMFLE! WHAT A MESS.
YUCK!
. . . MAKE SURE YOU'RE A PIG.

GNASHER and GNIPPER
STRIKE it LUCKY!
GNOW, GNOW, SON. BE CAREFUL DIGGING OR YOU'LL HIT A WOTSIT!
DIG!
RUMBLE!
AUSTRALIA, DAD?
GNOO-ER!
SPLOOOOSH!
GNYIPPEE! OIL! WE'RE RICH! RICH! OIL!

OIL!
GWOW!
So —
GOTTA BUILD A PLATFORM LIKE THE GNORTH SEA OIL RIGS!
GNEED THIS WOOD.

GURGLE!
WHAT'LL WE BUY WITH THE MONEY?
AND TREES!
GNICE THINKING!
FINISHED! WHAT A GREAT OIL RIG!
SCRATCH!
SCRATCH!
THAT'S COOL, DAD. MARK OUT THE HELIPAD.
Then —
DON'T BE ANGRY, DAD. IT'S OIL!
WHIR!
NO. BUT THE BLOK
WHO OWNS THE
TREACLE FACTORY
GNOO-ER!
POLICE

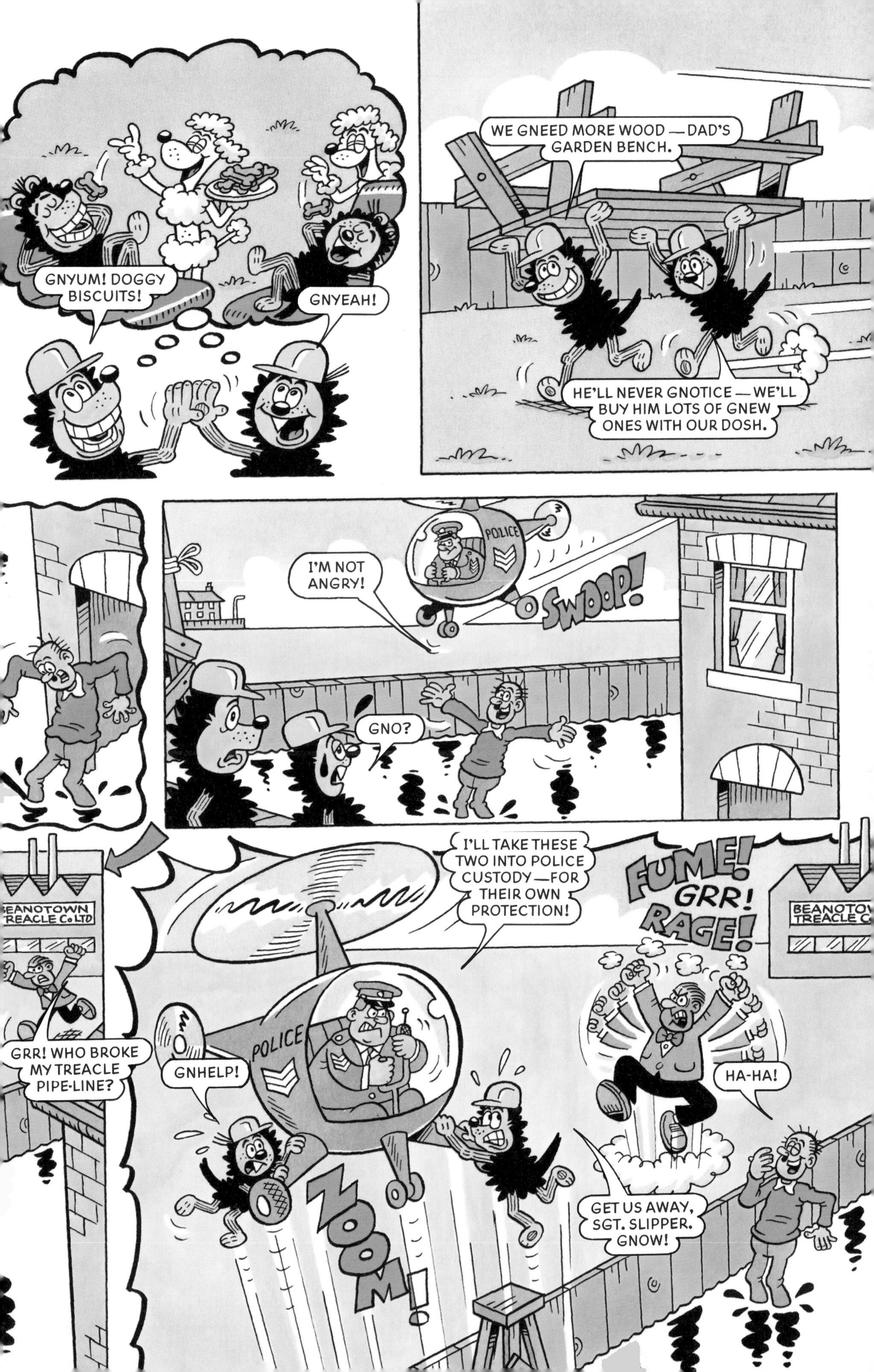
GNYUM! DOGGY BISCUITS!
GNYEAH!
WE GNEED MORE WOOD — DAD'S GARDEN BENCH.
HE'LL NEVER GNOTICE — WE'LL BUY HIM LOTS OF GNEW ONES WITH OUR DOSH.
POLICE
I'M NOT ANGRY!
SWOOP!
GNO?
BEANOTOWN TREACLE Co LTD
GRR! WHO BROKE MY TREACLE PIPE-LINE?
I'LL TAKE THESE TWO INTO POLICE CUSTODY—FOR THEIR OWN PROTECTION!
FUME! GRR! RAGE!
POLICE
GNHELP!
HA-HA!
ZOOM!
GET US AWAY, SGT. SLIPPER. GNOW!

GNASHER'S BIG CAT SAFARI

2 THE CHEETAH

GNIPPER? HE'S GNUTS!

The NORMAN CONQUEST
PART 2

RIGHT! I'M GOING TO PROVE TO THE MENACE THAT I'M THE BAD LAD IN THE DENNIS BOOK — ME, NASTY NORMAN!

I CHALLENGE YOU TO THE MENACE TEST!
EH?

HAR-HAR! WHAT'S YOUR ANSWER?

I ACCEPT!
WHAP!
DOOF!
GNOORAY!

FIRST, THE WATER DUEL.
I'M READY.
TWENTY PACES, TURN AND FIRE, RIGHT?
. . . 19 . . . 20! AW, THE WATER DIDN'T REACH.
RIGHT, GNASHER!
THAT'S BECAUSE YOU CHOSE THE WRONG KIND OF WATER SHOOTER!
GLOOPYA!
I'M NOT BEATEN YET — NEXT IS THE ROTTEN TOMATO FIGHT.
ULP! THAT'S MY LAST TOMATO!
MISSED!
DUCK
I'LL BE SAFE IN HERE, THOUGH.
DON'T YOU BELIEVE IT!
HE MUST BE OUT OF AMMO NOW!
SPLAT!
ERK! NO, HE WASN'T!
HAW-HAW! A REAL MENACE DOESN'T MAKE MISTAKES LIKE THAT!
NOW FOR THE FINAL TEST — ROUND UP A SOFTY, GNASHER!
ERM . . .
SO —
GASP! LOOK AT NORMAN! TITTER! GIGGLE!
CAN'T EVEN SCARE A SOFTY ANYMORE!
NOW THAT'S WHAT I CALL MENACING!
GLARE
HELP! MUMSIE!
SOB! I'M A FAILURE!

PING PONG? NOT FOR LONG!
NICE, WOOLLY PING PONG BATS—NOW WE CAN PLAY A GENTLE GAME OF TABLE TENNIS.
LOVELY!
CLICK!
CLICK!
NOT TOO HARD NOW, BERTIE.
SORRY, WATIKINS.
PIT!
PAT!
SUDDENLY—
SQUEAL!
PING!
RATATAT!
SNIGGER!
WAH! A GUN THAT FIRES PING PONG BALLS!

BURBLE!
I KNOW WHERE TO FIND MORE AMMO!

AT THE FAIRGROUND—
AHA!
LEGS—ELEVEN!
BINGO

SO—
UNLUCKY FOR SOME—DENNIS THE MENACE!
RATATAT!
EEK!

BACK HOME—
HANDS UP, DAD!
BAH! PING PONG BALLS CAN'T HARM ME!

YEEK! EGGS!
YES! AND THEY WERE FOR TEA!
RATATAT!
SPLAT!
GNEE! GNEE!
SPLOT!

TO YOUR BED, MENACE— WITHOUT SUPPER!
BOO!
GNEE! GNEE!

AND YOU GET TO YOUR KENNEL FOR LAUGHING!
GN-AW!

UPSTAIRS—
POOR GNASHER DIDN'T DO ANYTHING NAUGHTY!

ONLY FAIR, EH?
MY FAVOURITES— CHOCCY-DROPS! CHOMPITTY-CHOMP!
RATATAT!

PART 3
THE NORMAN CONQUEST

TUM-TEE-TUM!
THEN—
I'M NORMAN— NASTIEST PERSON IN "THE BEANO" AND YOU'RE GOING TO GET THUMPED! AH-SO!
CHOP
OH, YES?
KICK

GRAB
ULP! THIS ISN'T WHAT I PLANNED!
HOPPITY-HOP

HOO-HA-HA-CACKLE! STOP IT, YOU R-ROTTER!
TICKLE

YOU DON'T KNOW WHO YOU'RE DEALING WITH—WATCH ME BREAK THIS PLANK WITH ONE HAND!
SWISH!
WHAT A WALLY—I KNEW THAT WOULD HAPPEN!
SQUASH!
CHOP!
ANYWAY, I BROKE THE PLANK WITH ONE HAND— YOU COULDN'T!
HUH! I COULD BREAK A BRICK WITH JUST ONE TOOTH!
RUB
RUB

BET YOU COULDN'T!
GNIPPER!
YOWL!
I DIDN'T SAY WHICH TOOTH I'D USE!
BITE
CRUNCH!

NO MORE MISTER NICE GUY!
SUITS ME!
GRAB
GRAB
WAH!
HELP!
PUT YOUR PAW ON THAT, GNASHER— THANKS!

I DON'T KNOW ABOUT BEING THE NASTIEST PERSON IN "THE BEANO," NORMAN, BUT...

... YOU'RE CERTAINLY THE KNOTTIEST!
MUM!

STAND B
Starring Denni
IT'S A JUNGLE OUT THERE, I TELL YOU.
FIX!
CUT!
BUT MY TRUSTY BAYONET WILL SOON CLEAR MY OVERGROWN GARDEN!
FOLLOWED BY SOME TANK MANOEUVRES!
IT'S A WATER TANK, ACTUALLY!
GROW, YOU BLIGHTERS, GROW! THAT IS AN ORDER!
SO! DISOBEYING A DIRECT ORDER? YOU KNOW WHAT THAT MEANS!

UR FLOWERBEDS!

rmy army neighbour, The Colonel!

LET SLEEPING MENACES LIE!

TIME TO GET UP, DENNIS!
ZZZZZ!

SAME THING EVERY MORNING— I'VE GOT TO WAKEN UP THIS SLEEPY-HEAD!
ZZZZ!

SNIGGER!
ZZZZZ!
AND AN ICE-COLD SHOWER IS THE ONLY WAY TO DO IT!
WAH! BRRRR!

THAT NIGHT-
I WON'T GET A SHOWER TOMORROW-NOT AFTER I'VE TURNED OFF THE WATER!

NEXT MORNING-
I'M FED UP CARRYING DENNIS TO THE SHOWER. A BUCKET OF WATER WILL BE JUST AS GOOD TO WAKEN HIM!

WELL, IT WOULD - IF THERE WAS ANY WATER!

SO-
WAKEN UP, YOU DOZY DENNIS!
WHIP!

HEY! HE MUST BE UP ALREADY.

NO, HE ISN'T!
ZZZZ!

THIS MIGHT WORK!
TARRAPP!

ULP! PRETTY CLEVER! I'LL HAVE TO PLAN ANOTHER PLAN!
SILENCE
TWANG!

THAT'S IT-IT'S RAINING!

GNASHER! HERE, BOY!

THEN-
JUST AS I PLANNED!
HOWL!
SHAKE

SMUG
HUMPH! I THOUGHT YOU WERE SUPPOSED TO BE MY PAL!
ASHAMED

CRIMEWATCH O.K.?

FOLLOW THAT MENACE!
I'M TOO WELL-KNOWN, I NEED A DISGUISE, BUT I'VE GOT TO LOSE THIS LOT FIRST!

THE OLD "WASHER" DODGE FROM ROGER SHOULD DO THE TRICK!

IT WORKED! I'VE ESCAPED!
IT'S NOT A COIN - IT'S A WASHER!

BACK HOME -
NOW FOR MY DISGUISE - I NEED LOTS OF HAIR GEL...
SPLUT!

SOON -
...GOOD DISGUISE EH? I'M FREE TO HAVE FUN NOW!

SO -
EEK!
IT'S WALTER!
OW!

THEN -
HELP!
WAH!
SQUIRT!

SHORTLY -
IT WAS WALTER!
I DON'T BELIEVE IT - BUT WE'D BETTER ARREST WALTER ANYWAY!

SO -
I GOT WALTER, SERGEANT!
WANTED
I WANT MY MUMSY!
LOST

THEN -
SO DID I!
TWO WALTERS? EVEN WALTER'S DAD COULDN'T TELL WHICH IS THE REAL WALTER!
WANTED
BUT I CAN...
LOST

...THE ONLY THING YOU COULDN'T DISGUISE WERE YOUR KNEES - DENNIS!
ERK! CAUGHT BY DAD!

YOU'RE GOING TO JAIL - KEPT IN FOR A WEEK, MENACE!
IF YOU WANT TO BE REAL POLICEMEN, LEARN TO SPOT CLUES LIKE THAT!
TEE-HEE!
ULP!
CLEVER!

VISITING 'CARD!'

THIS WAY, READERS—I'VE GOT A TREAT FOR YOU.

VERY POSH OFFICES
EVEN MORE POSH OFFICES
I'M TAKING YOU TO VISIT "THE BEANO" OFFICE...

BLOW FOOTBALL
ZZZZZ!
THINK—BUT DO IT QUIETLY!
... AND THIS IS IT!
ZZZ!
IN
OUT
WAY OUT
EDITOR
CHIEF SUB
THE BEANO OFFICE
HI, MUM!
HELP! I'M A PRISONER AND BEING MADE TO READ "THE DANDY"!
NEW CAR CATALOGUE
MILK WAS
SUGAR

THERE'S THE FAMOUS OLIVE—SHE MAKES THE OFFICE TEA.
BURBLE!
HEY! CALAMITY JAMES HAS BEEN LOOKING FOR THIS SOCK!
TEA
SUGAR
I THINK WE'LL SKIP THE TEA—THAT'S WHAT I MAKE MY HOME-MADE STINK BOMBS FROM!
THAT'S THE EDITOR—HIS HOBBY'S PLAYING GOLF—IN FACT, I THINK THAT'S HIS JOB!
FORE!
FIVE!
THAT'S THE ARTIST WHO DRAWS ME—HIS HOBBY'S GOLF AS WELL.
HEY, JOE, ALONG THE WATCHTOWER IN A PURPLE HAZE—YEAH!
UNCLE AL WRITES MY STORIES! HIS HOBBY'S PLAYING GUITAR—
BADLY!
ALL OF WHICH ISN'T VERY EXCITING—SO I'M GOING TO LIVEN THINGS UP!
SEVEN!
SIX!
SNIP!
TWANG!
UNCLE AL
OOPS!
EIGHTEEEEK!
CRACK!
THWACK!
LASH!
BONK!
CRACK!
PING!
AMBULANCE
BEANO BUILDING
MOAN!
WELL, I CERTAINLY LIVENED THINGS UP...
I'VE GOT TO DO ALL THEIR JOBS TILL THEY GET BETTER!
SCRIPT
EVERYONE WE KNOW READS "THE BEANO"!

WE'LL SUPPORT YOU EVERMORE!
But which teams do the BEANO stars follow?
Gnasher supports WOLVES
MEE-OH, OH, OH!
ZOOM!
GRR!
SNARL!
GNRRR!
SLAVER!
THAT LUMP OF HAM HAS EATEN TONS OF TURNIPS!
ME'S TOTALLY FULL!
BULGE
Rasher supports FULHAM
YEE-OW!
YEE-HAR!
PRANG!
Dennis supports SPURS

BOOM!
BLAST!
WAH! BOO-HOO! MY CRYSTAL — RUINED! MY HOME! MY PALACE — RUINED!
CRASH!
SMASH!
TINKLE!
The Dinmakers support CRYSTAL PALACE
STOMP!
Bea supports BLACKPOOL
OO! WHAT A MESS!
ME'S LOVIN' IT!
OH, BEA!

HA-HA!
THIS IS THE ONLY WAY WE CAN KEEP THIS LOT OUT OF MISCHIEF!
BAH! BLOOMIN' PARENTS!
Mum and Dad support LEADS
GNOT GNICE!

SAY CHEESE PLEASE!
IT'S ABOUT TIME WE HAD AN UP-TO-DATE PICTURE OF DENNIS.
YOU'RE RIGHT, DEAR.
SO—
I'M NOT SURE WHAT'S GOING ON, BUT I DON'T THINK I LIKE IT!
SOON—
PHOTOGRAPHER
HE'S ALL YOURS, MR BAILEY.
NOW I KNOW I DON'T LIKE IT— I HATE HAVING MY PHOTOGRAPH TAKEN!

WILL I SIT OVER THERE?
FINE!
THIS IS GOING TO BE EASIER THAN I THOUGHT, I THINK.
WAH!
SNIGGER!
CLICK!
COLLAPSES
MAYBE IT'S NOT GOING TO BE AS EASY AS I THOUGHT.
TAP-TAP!
SIT UP STRAIGHT, MENACE!
MUST SHOW HIM WHO'S BOSS!
HOLD IT! THE CARPET'S SQUINT—I'LL STRAIGHTEN IT!
OOH, THANKS.
YIKES!
CLICK!
CACKLE!
TUG!
ZIP!
ON—
I'LL DISTRACT HIS ATTENTION!
WATCH THE BIRDIE!
SQUIRT!
SQUIRT!
GLUB!
THAT DOES IT!
I THOUGHT THE BIRDIE COULD DO WITH A DRINK!
TER—
WELL, I MANAGED TO TAKE THE PHOTOGRAPH, BUT I DON'T THINK YOU'LL LIKE IT!
YOU DON'T?
IT WAS THE ONLY WAY I COULD GET HIM TO SIT STILL!
OOOH, DENNIS!

ARE YOU THE GREAT SGT. SLIPPER?
WHIRR!
SGT. SLIPPE
OF THE YAR
GLORY DAYS. BUT THEN I WAS TRANSFERRED TO BEANOTOWN.
HELP US!
PLEASE!
GO ON!
WHIRR!
OF COURSE, WITH MY POLICE SKILLS AND SHARP BRAIN, I SOON WORKED OUT WHO THE PROBLEM-MAKERS WERE!
WANTED
THEM!
WHIRR!

— ALAS!
FZZT!
POLICE
BOOM!
SPLAT!
CUSTARD FLAN

YOU SEE, IT WASN'T REALLY GNASHER.
YOU GREAT BLITHERING TWIT! I'M UNDERCOVER, TRYING TO CATCH THE MENACES!
CHIEF CONSTABLE IN GNASHER COSTUME
OH, MY!

ER, WELL, I USED TO BE!
WOW! SGT. SLIPPER HAS CAUGHT THE HOLE IN THE DOOR GANG!
BAIL JUMPERS
CROOKS
MUGGERS
SCRAPE!
ILLEGAL PARKERS
TUG.
SLIPPER OF THE YARD — OUR HERO!
NEW SCOTLAND YARD
SPIN
GNASHER WILL GO FOR THIS.
JUICY STEAK
BRILLIANT!
WHIRR!
MY PLAN WORKED A TREAT—
GNYUM!
TAP!
WHIRR!

SO, I USED TO BE SLIPPER OF THE YARD.
AND NOW?
I'M SLIPPER OF MY BACK YARD! SSSH! HE MIGHT HEAR US!
WHERE IS THAT SILLY OIK? GRRR!
SWISH!
WHIRR
SILENT TITTERS!

RECIPE-FOR DISASTER!

TODAY I'LL SHOW YOU A RECIPE —FIRST TAKE A PEA . . .

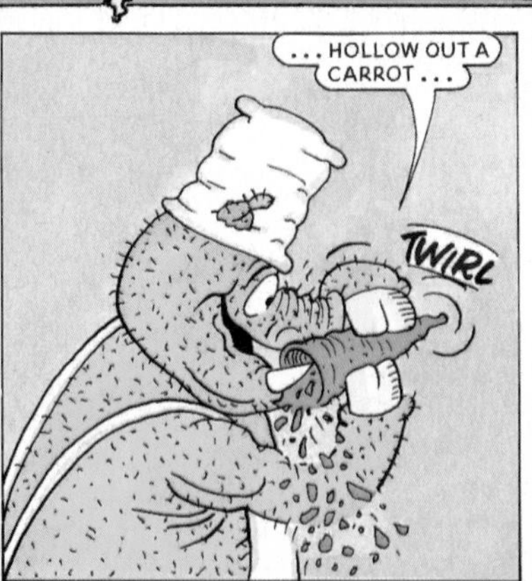
. . . HOLLOW OUT A CARROT . . .
TWIRL

. . . AND ADD THE PEA.
SWEEP
PLOP!

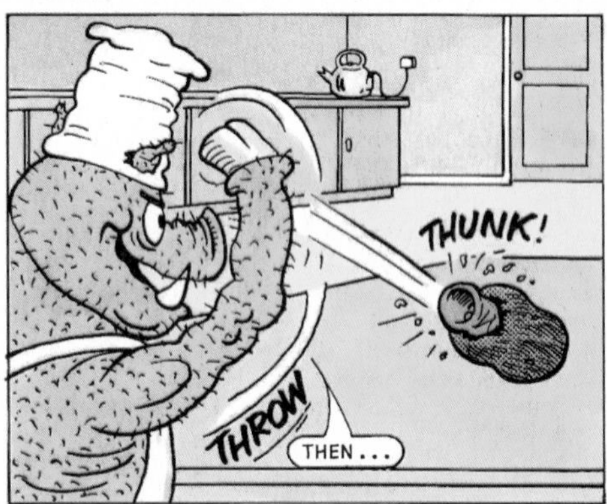
THUNK!
THROW
THEN . . .

. . . STUFF A POTATO THE QUICK WAY.

NOW PUT THE POTATO ON A TURNIP.

AND SIT ON IT.
SQUASH

GOOD, EH?

THEN PUT THE TURNIP IN A CABBAGE, THE CABBAGE IN A CAULIFLOWER, THE CAULIFLOWER IN A MARROW, THE MARROW IN A PUMPKIN.
SQUASH

BE CAREFUL, THOUGH . . .
SQUASH

. . . THAT YOU DON'T STUFF IT TOO TIGHT.
EXPLODE

EH?
LICK
LICK
MIND YOU THIS IS A GREAT WAY TO EAT STUFFED PUMPKIN.

GNICE FACE PAINT. ARE YOU AN INJUN, TOO?
GNASHER'S
BIG CAT
SAFARI
3 THE TIGER

BROLLY GOOD SHOW!
DAD'S BROLLY WAS BEING REPAIRED— I HAD TO COLLECT IT.
SOON—
OO! SUCH JOLLY FUN!
WALTER— SOFTER THAN TOILET TISSUE.
MAYBE I COULD HAVE SOME FUN WITH THIS UMBRELLA.

SNIGGER!
SQUEAL!
GNEE-HEE!

MUMSY! I'M ALL WET!
HAW-HAW!

SOON—
WELL, WELL! NASTY NORMAN, BENEATH THE SPREADING CHESTNUT TREE.
YAH! ONLY SOFTIES CARRY BROLLIES.

WHAT ARE YOU KICKING THE TREE FOR?

HEH-HEH!
OOYAH! CHESTNUTS! I'LL GET YOU FOR THIS!
Norman's rocket

YOU'LL HAVE TO CATCH ME FIRST!
Norman's rocket Beware

GREAT! IT EVEN GOES UP HILL. A BIT DIFFICULT FOR ...
Beware Norman's rocket

... STEERING, THOUGH! ARGH! THORNS!
Norman's rocket Beware

I'M FED UP CARRYING THIS— YOU TAKE IT, GNASHER.

BACK HOME—
NNNF! YOU CAN LET GO NOW!
GNEE-HEE! I LOVE A TUG OF WAR!

AND SOON—
RAIN! LUCKY I HAVE MY REPAIRED BROLLY.

DENNIS!

BRACE YOURSELF!
I'M BORED! I'M FED UP! I'M CHEESED OFF!
CAN I HAVE MONEY FOR THE CINEMA, DAD? I'M BORED, DAD! DAD? HOI! WAKEN UP, DAD!
THIS'LL GET HIS ATTENTION! SNIGGER!
STRETCH!
NNNNNGH!
WHAP!
TWANG!

CAN I HAVE MONEY FOR THE CINEMA?
NO! IN MY DAY WE MADE OUR OWN ENTERTAINMENT— YOU CAN DO IT AS WELL!
MAKE MY OWN ENTERTAINMENT, EH? I THINK I CAN DO THAT.
ZZZZ
DAD WON'T MISS THESE WHILE HE'S SNOOZING!
GRR! I WAS SAVING THAT— IT'S MY BEST 1975 VINTAGE TURNIP!
RASHER
I SHOT A TURNIP INTO THE AIR...
STRETCH
...IT FELL TO EARTH ON A SOFTY'S HAIR!
SQUELCH!
WAH!
STRETCH
GOOD ENTERTAINMENT, THAT— NOW I'LL MAKE SOME MORE.
HERE I GO...
ZOOM!
...YAHOO! BETTER THAN THE FUNFAIR!
ZZZZ
I CAN MAKE GREAT ENTERTAINMENT, BUT I'D BETTER GET THE BRACES BACK BEFORE DAD NOTICES!
LATER—
DENNIS! HAVE YOU BEEN MESSING WITH MY BRACES?
HE'S NOTICED...
... BUT HE'S EVEN BETTER AT MAKING ENTERTAINMENT THAN I AM!
BLUSH!
SNIGGER!
GIGGLE!
TH-THEY'RE ALL STRETCHED!

MENACING IN A WINTER WONDERLAND!
BAH! WISH IT WAS SUMMER.
GNESH!
OUTDOOR SWIMMING POOL
I'LL JUST HAVE TO DO SUMMERY THINGS.
WAY IN

YAHOO! GREAT FUN!
CHANGING ROOMS
WATER SLIDE

THAT SHOULD BE ENOUGH COAL FOR THE WINTER.
HMM!

MORE SUMMER FUN— THIS IS NEARLY AS GOOD AS REAL SURFING.
RUMBLE!
ZOOM!
CRASH!

EXT—
AND THE MENACE COMES IN TO BOWL...

WHEEEEE!
SPLAT!
OW!
... WHAT A BOWLER—HE'S HIT THE MIDDLE STUMP...

... AND KNOCKED OFF THE BAILS!
CRUNCH!

EEK!
OW!
CACKLE!
ROTTEN MENACE! I'LL HELP YOU TO PAY HIM BACK!

READY—AIM...
ULP!
... FIRE!

VERY MUDDY SPLUDGE!

SOON—
GOODNESS! I THOUGHT IT WAS WINTER—HOW DID DENNIS MANAGE TO GET SUCH A SUPER TAN?
HUMPH!

LOOK OUT, LONDON!

The Menace family are sight-seeing in London.
SIGHT-SEEING TOUR OF LONDON
COR! THIS BUS IS OPEN-TOPPED. JUST THE KIND THE CUP WINNERS SHOW OFF THE CUP WITH!
SEE: THE DOME ST PAUL'S HER MAJEST GAFF BIG BEN SMALL FRED TINY TIMMY

WE WON THE CUP! WE WON THE CUP!
Bea's Potty CONTENTS: Best NOT ask!
EH?

OOPS. I SEEM TO HAVE SPILLED SOME. OH, DEAR. PITY.
HEE-HEE-HEE! NICE ONE, BRUVVER!
1
LONDON
1
QUEUE HERE TO SEE LONDON (AND GET USED TO QUEUEING!)
AND YOU CAN SEE LONDON'S WORLD FAMOUS STOCK EXCHANGE!
BORING!
STOCK EXCHANGE, HUH?
WE'LL EXCHANGE STOCK WITH THEM! CHEW, LADS!
GYUM!
Marble Arch
Yo-yo Arch
TIDDLY-WINK ARCH
EEK!
FIRE!
PTOO!
ONDON
HEE-HEE! NICE 'UN — STOCK CUBES!
THE STOCK EXCHANGE
THERE! A WELL-STOCKED STOCK EXCHANGE!
AND THAT IS NELSON'S COLUMN!
LET'S HAVE A PHOTO OF ME AND NELSON, SIDE BY SIDE.

GNZZZZZZZ
THINK THE STATUE IS TOO TALL?
SAY 'CHEESY FEET'!
NO WAY — JUST RIGHT!

WHAT'S THE TOP SPEED?

QUITE QUICK, ACTUALLY!
WAHEY!
NIGEL PARKINSON

DON'T WORRY, MENACE PARENTS. I KNOW WHERE TO TAKE THEM NOW!
OH, YES, WELL, ER . . .

JUST BIG ENOUGH FOR A DOUBLE-DECKER
THIS DOESN'T LOOK LIKE A TOURIST ATTRACTION.
CLOSE ALL WINDOWS
IN
GNUH? LIKE A GARAGE!

AARGH! WORSE!

OH, ME! WHAT NEXT, MENACES?
BUCKINGHAM PALACE!
And —
WOW! SHE'S GOT A NICE MOTOR!
LOVELY SETTA WHEELS!
NICE! TA, QUEEN!
WHEEZE!
YOU CAN USE MY MENACE CAR ANY TIME!
TA, DEN!
I'VE SEEN THE QUEEN

CAR WASH
LONDON
THE MENACES HAVE BEEN SO GOOD, I'LL GET THEM A JOB IN LONDON!
REALLY?

Yes! As London Zoo's new exhibits!
THIS IS LONDON ZOO
AND YOU'RE WELCOME TO IT!
NO ESCAPED LIONS FOR 10 DAYS
MYSTERY CAGE!
IRAFFE
GORILLA
SNAKE HOUSE
RAT RANCH
HYENA HOTEL
BADGER BUNGALOW
FOX FLATS
POLAR BEAR
WELL, WHAT ARE THEY?
WASH-OUTS! HA-HA!
NO IDEA!
SUGGESTION BOX
WHAT IS IT ?

GOOSEY GOOSEY OO-ER!

THIS SHOP HAS A GUARD GOOSE
I THINK I'LL PINCH A SAUSAGE.

OUT! OUT!
PECK

NOBODY DOES THAT TO ME!

WOW! IT CAN FLY!
SCREECH!

MUST TRY THAT!
FLAP

WOW! I CAN FLY!

THIS IS GREAT!

GNWAH! MY WINGS HAVE STOPPED WORKING.

SPLOT!

I'LL DRY HIM OFF.
WAFT

STRAIN
GNIPPER CAN'T FLY, BUT HE STILL KNOWS HOW A BIRD FEELS . . .

. . . HE'S JUST HATCHED FROM AN EGG!
CRACK!

'WOOD' YOU BELIEVE IT?

TIMBER? NO HE COULDN'T HAVE— MAYBE I'D BETTER CHECK THOUGH.
TIMBER MERCHANTS
A. LOG. FIREWOOD
SOLD

ARGH! HE **DID!**
CRUNCH!

SOLD OUT
THROB!
AMBULANCE
MY FAVOURITE TREE—GONE! MY PET CORN—SQUASHED!
LETS GO, DOGS!

IT'S MUCH EASIER GOING DOWNHILL!
TRUNDLE!

OH, CRUMBS! IT'S NOT AS EASY AS I THOUGHT!
BRAKE!
SKID!

OOPS!
SNAP!
SNAP!
GNERK!

MAYBE I CAN BEAT IT!
ZOOM!

DAD! DAD! OPEN THE DOOR!
THUMP!

JUST IN TIME! AT LEAST WE'VE GOT PLENTY OF FUEL IN THE HOUSE NOW!
EEK!
LEAP TO SAFETY

BE A SPORT!
YAH, BOO— CAN'T GET TO ME!
I CAN'T REACH THAT HEIGHT...
POLITE RASP!
ZOOM!
?

...BUT I CAN POLE VAULT!
WAH!
SPLAT!
SPLAT!
SPLAT!
SPLAT!
BLOW!
SPLAT!
SPLAT!
PTCHEEEEEEE

A MENACE HAS TO BE GOOD AT SPORTS.
SLIDE

I'LL TELL YOUR DADDY, LADDIE! YOU'VE BEEN MENACING DEAR WATIKINS.
OH! ULP! WALTER'S UNCLE!

HERE'S ANOTHER KIND OF VAULT! SOME GYMNASTICS!
LEAP
GOT YOU— BAH!

OOPS! SHOULD HAVE LOOKED BEFORE I LEAPT!
BOUNCE
EEK!

STILL, HE GETS 9 OUT OF 10 FOR THAT DIVE!
PIE-SHOP
CHOMP!
WAH!

PIE-SHOP
RUGBY'S A GOOD SPORT FOR A MENACE!

ESPECIALLY WHEN YOU WANT TO...

...SEPARATE ONE OF YOUR PALS FROM HIS LAST PIE. CHOMP!

LATER-
OF COURSE, A MENACE SHOULDN'T NEGLECT THE THROWING SPORTS —— LIKE THROWING THE HAMMER...

...OR IN THIS CASE, NASTY NORMAN!
GRRR!
GNEE-GNEE!
SPLUDGE!

MOSTLY, THOUGH, A MENACE SHOULD BE GOOD AT JUMPING...

GURR!
GRR!
OR AT LEAST, KEEPING ONE JUMP AHEAD OF THIS LOT!
JUMP
JUMP

HAIR TODAY-GONE TODAY!

OH-OH, GNASHER'S TEETH ARE STARTING TO CHATTER!
CHATTER
AND WITH TEETH AS BIG AS GNASHER'S THAT MEANS... TROUBLE!
CHATTER-CHATTER!
NEVER MIND, I'LL STICK THIS HAIR BACK ON.
HMMM...
CHATTER
AH! JUST WHAT I NEED FOR STUFFING PILLOWS, DENNIS—THANKS!
EH?
GRAB
CHATTER
SNORE! GRUNT!
GULP! HAVE TO THINK OF SOME OTHER WAY TO REPLACE GNASHER'S HAIR.
WOOM!
DAD'S JERSEY WILL COME IN HANDY.
RIP
TUG
SNIP! SNIP! SNIP!
RIGHT, GNASHER!
SPLOT!
PASTE
NOW, ROLL OVER!
ROLL
ROLL
NOT QUITE RIGHT, IS IT?
BELLOW!
GURRR!
COAL SHED
ZOOM
DAD'S FOUND OUT ABOUT THE JERSEY, SO WE'D BETTER HIDE IN HERE FOR A WHILE.
PRESENTLY—
COAL SHED
YOU'LL BE ABLE TO RECOGNISE GNASHER NOW, READERS.
GNYES! BUT WILL THEY RECOGNISE YOU?

SOOTS YOU!
TITTER! GIGGLE!
WHEN GNASHER GOT STUCK
UP THE CHIMNEY,
HE BEGAN TO SQUIRM.
A SOFTY BOY
WAS FILLED WITH JOY—
THE HORRID LITTLE WORM.
THE SILLY DOGGY
WAS CHASING A MOGGY
AND NOW HE'S STUCK
UP THE FLUE.
WHEN GNASHER GOT STUCK
UP THE CHIMNEY,
BOO-HOO! BOO-HOO!
BOO-HOO!

PUFF!
SNOW CLOUD
SNOW CLOUD
TUMBLE
WHEN GNASHER GOT STUCK UP THE CHIMNEY, HE BEGAN TO SNEEZE. A CLOUD OF SOOT, STRAIGHT UP DID SHOOT— GOT CARRIED ON THE BREEZE...
ALMIGHTY SNEEZE!
I'M UNSTUCK!
B-BLACK SNOW? WHAT'S GOING ON?
... A FALL OF SNOW GOT MIXED UP BELOW— THE SOFTY HADN'T A CLUE.
SNIGGER! WHATEVER'S GOING ON IS GOING ALL ON YOU!
WHIMPER!
WHEN GNASHER GOT STUCK UP THE CHIMNEY— GNACHOO! GNACHOO! GNACHOO!
Soots you? Oh! SUITS YOU — over the page!

YOU'VE READ 'SOOTS YOU', NOW TRY
SUITS YOU
IT'S ALL ABOUT MENACING CLOTHES!
GNASHIN' FASHION!
TURN-UPS
HEE-HEE! LOVELY TURN UPS, ER, TURNIPS!
SPLAT
SQUEAL! ONE'S JERSEY!
SPLURT
KIPPER TIES
LIKE IT, DENNIS?
TANK TOPS
WAHEY! THIS TANK TOP IS COOL!
PING!
PING!
PING!
SHRIEK!
I SAY!
TOUGH BOY'S SWIMMING POOL

SWEATERS
LEISURE CENTRE SAUNAS
SWEAT
SWEAT
SWEAT
CLICK!
CLICK!
WAH!
CLICK!
PUSH
PUSH
KICK
SWEAT IT OUT, SOFTIES!
YER — BUT THIS KIPPER IS MORE FUN!
FISHY PONG!
SMELLY SPLODGE
WHIMPER!
T-SHIRTS
T-SHIRTS?
NO — TEA BAGS!
JUMPERS
PLOP!
PLOP!
PLOP!

A (S)POT OF BOTHER!

MERRY CHRISTMAS
HEH-HEH!
DO YOURSELF A FAVOUR, ALL YOU GIRL READERS!
TIP-TOE

SPLOT!
DENNIS, REMOVE THAT, AT ONCE!
SIGH, OK!
MM!
PULL!
HEY! IT'S STUCK PRETTY TIGHT.
HEAVE
WHEEEEE!
SHLOP!
DONE IT!
OOPS!
PLOP!
HAW-HAW-HAW! THAT SERVES YOU RIGHT.
I DON'T KNOW WHY YOU'RE LAUGHING, DEAR.
WHY NOT?
YOUR CHRISTMAS PUDDING IS IN THAT POT!
WHAT?
WHY ARE YOU SO HAPPY, DENNIS?
SNIGGER!
BECAUSE OLIVE, THE BASH ST. COOK MADE IT-WITH TURNIPS AND CEMENT! SO-
HO-HO!
SO-
RAZZZZZ!
NNNNNG!
ICE CREAM
MERRY CHRISTMAS READERS
POP
POP
CHALKS
-I WON'T HAVE TO EAT THE DISGUSTING MUCK!

GNASHER'S BIG CAT SAFARI

4 THE LION

SLIDE ON DENNIS!

SLIDING'S GREAT FUN

AND I'M PUTTING A STOP TO HIS FUN.
SALT
SIZZLE
SALT
OOF!
WHIZZZZZZ!
SCREEECH TO A HALT!

TH-THAT WAS T-TERRIBLE-GASP!
HUH! IT WAS EVEN WORSE THAN THAT...

...THE SUDDEN STOP TORE THE SOLES OFF MY BOOTS-LOOK!
LOOK? I CAN SMELL-POOH!

IT'S YOUR FAULT DENNIS'S BOOTS GOT RUINED-SO YOU CAN CARRY HIM TO THE SHOE SHOP!
SIGH! YES DEAR.

SO-
ARGH! IT LOOKS LIKE THE MENACE NEEDS NEW SHOES-
EMERGENCY!
BOYS' SHOES

PHEW! WE'RE SAFE!
BOYS' SHOES

BUT-
SNIGGER! YOU FORGOT ABOUT THE BACK DOOR!
ULP! I SUPPOSE I'LL HAVE TO SERVE HIM AS I'M THE MANAGER.
FAINT

SOON-
THESE FEEL COMFY BUT I'D BETTER TEST THEM.
EH?

FIRST-JUMPING!
WHUMP!
THUD!

TOPPLE
NEXT...
HELP!

...KICKING!
WHAP!

LATEST STYLES
SHOES TO CHOOSE
BOP!
BOP!
BOP!

S-SIR, Y-YOUR SON'S F-FEET A-ARE KILLING ME!
GREAT!

GOODNIGHT, READERS!
DON'T FORGET! YOU CAN SEE DENNIS AND GNASHER IN THE BEANO— EVERY THURSDAY!
DON'T WORRY. US ELEPHANTS NEVER FORGET. ER, NOW, DID I BRUSH MY TEETH?... DID I PUT THE CAT OUT?... DID I LEAVE A NOTE FOR THE MILKMAN? OO-ER!

JOIN THE ARMY
BEANO-TOWN
RIVER PATROL